B flat instruments edition

For Clarinet, Trumpet, Cornet & Tenor Sax
plus chords for Guitar & Keyboard

Kevin
Mayhew

We hope you enjoy *A Pocketful of Tunes* for B flat instruments.
Further copies of this and the other books in the series
are available from your local music shop.

In case of difficulty, please contact the publisher direct:

The Sales Department
KEVIN MAYHEW LTD
Buxhall
Stowmarket
Suffolk IP14 3DJ

Phone 01449 737978
Fax 01449 737834

Please ask for our complete catalogue of outstanding Instrumental Music.

First published in Great Britain in 1995 by Kevin Mayhew Ltd

© Copyright 1995 Kevin Mayhew Ltd

ISBN 0 86209 718 5
Catalogue No: 3611174

1 2 3 4 5 6 7 8 9

Cover design by Neil Pinchbeck
Music edited and arranged by Donald Thomson
Music setting: Daniel Kelly

Printed and bound in Great Britain

AIR from SUITE NO 3

Johann Sebastian Bach

WALTZING MATILDA

Marie Cowan

MICHAEL, ROW THE BOAT ASHORE
Traditional Melody

JERUSALEM
Charles Hubert Parry

AMAZING GRACE
Traditional American Melody

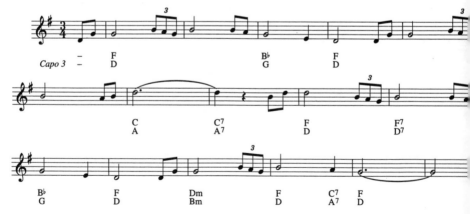

ALL THE NICE GIRLS LOVE A SAILOR
A J Mills and Bennett Scott

GREENSLEEVES
Anonymous 17th Century Melody

RULE, BRITANNIA
Thomas Arne

BLOW THE WIND SOUTHERLY
Traditional English Melody

THE DRUNKEN SAILOR
Sea Shanty

ODE TO JOY
Ludwig van Beethoven

11

THE KEEL ROW
Traditional English Melody

Capo 3

–	F	B♭	F	C	F	B♭	F	C	F
–	D	G	D	A	D	G	D	A	D

B♭	F	C	F	B♭	F	C7	F
G	D	A	D	G	D	A7	D

O SOLE MIO
Eduardo di Capua

–   C   G7

C   Fm

C   G7   C

SCARBOROUGH FAIR
Traditional English Melody

Dm   A   Dm   G   Dm

Am   F   C   Dm   Gm   Am   Dm

THE FLOWERS THAT BLOOM IN THE SPRING

Arthur Sullivan

LULLABY

Johannes Brahms

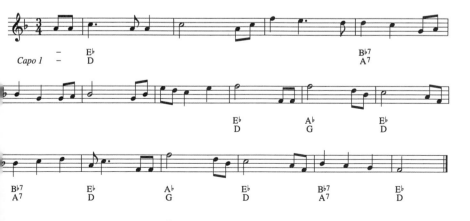

A LIFE ON THE OCEAN WAVE

Henry Russell

Capo 3

COCKLES AND MUSSELS

Traditional Irish Melody

Capo 3

SCÈNE from 'SWAN LAKE'

Peter Ilyich Tchaikovsky

AULD LANG SYNE

Traditional Scottish Melody

THE YELLOW ROSE OF TEXAS
Traditional American Melody

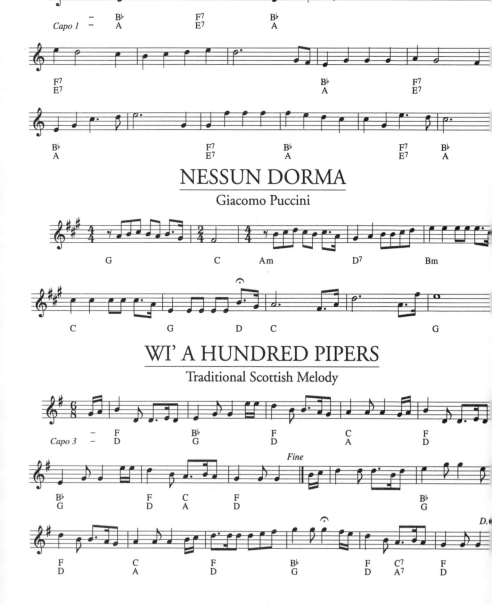

NESSUN DORMA
Giacomo Puccini

WI' A HUNDRED PIPERS
Traditional Scottish Melody

ROMANZA

Anon

LITTLE BROWN JUG

R A Eastburn

SHAKER SONG
Traditional American Melody

TRUMPET VOLUNTARY
Jeremiah Clarke

RONDO from HORN CONCERTO K495

Wolfgang Amadeus Mozart

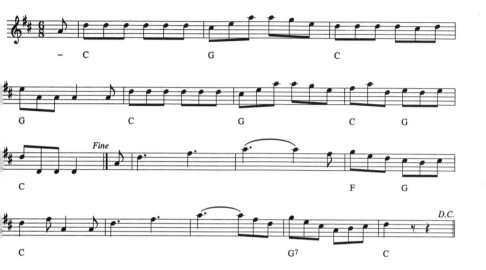

NOBODY KNOWS THE TROUBLE I SEE

Spiritual

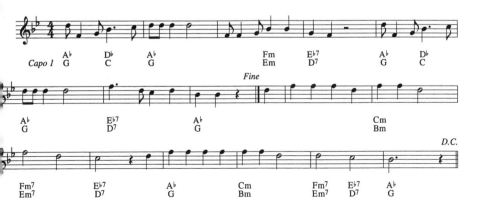

WILLIAM TELL OVERTURE
Gioachino Rossini

THE ENTERTAINER
Scott Joplin

CAPRICE
Nicolo Paganini

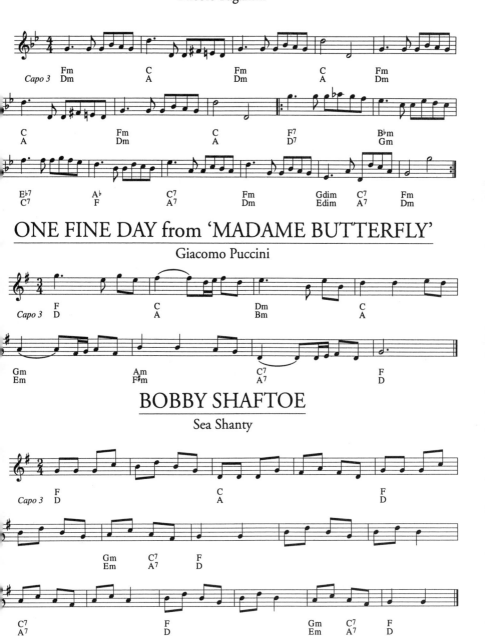

ONE FINE DAY from 'MADAME BUTTERFLY'
Giacomo Puccini

BOBBY SHAFTOE
Sea Shanty

21

PANIS ANGELICUS

César Franck

THE BLUE BELL OF SCOTLAND

Traditional Scottish Melody

HUNGARIAN DANCE NO 5

Johannes Brahms

CLEMENTINE

Percy Montrose

MEN OF HARLECH

Traditional Welsh Melody

TOREADOR'S SONG from 'CARMEN'

Georges Bizet

DANCE OF THE HOURS
Amilcare Ponchielli

LA CUCARACHA
Traditional Mexican Melody

OH DEAR, WHAT CAN THE MATTER BE?
Traditional Melody

DANNY BOY

Traditional Irish Melody

FÜR ELISE

Ludwig van Beethoven

YE BANKS AND BRAES

Traditional Scottish Melody

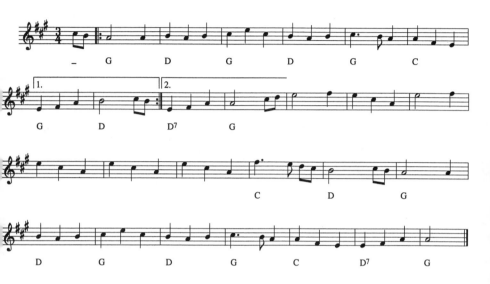

MANGO WALK

Jamaican Folk Song

27

PARADE OF THE TIN SOLDIERS

Leon Jessel

THEME from SYMPHONY NO 1

Johannes Brahms

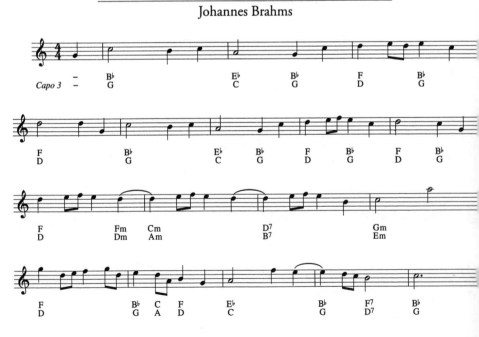

EINE KLEINE NACHTMUSIK
Wolfgang Amadeus Mozart

THE CAN CAN
Jacques Offenbach

GLORY, GLORY HALLELUJAH
William Stäffe

- C   F   C

E⁷   Am   Dm   G⁷   C   C⁷

F   C   E⁷   Am   Dm   G⁷   C

MORNING HAS BROKEN
Traditional Gaelic Melody

C   Am   Dm   G   F   C

F   C   G   C   Am   Dm   C

Am   Dm   C   F   G   C

DADDY WOULDN'T BUY ME A BOW-WOW
Joseph Tabrar

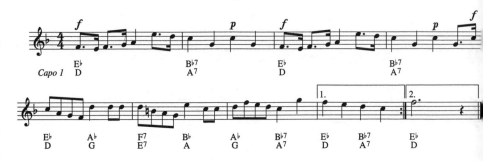

f   *p*   *f*   *p*   *f*

Capo 1   E♭   B♭⁷   E♭   B♭⁷
    D   A⁷   D   A⁷

E♭   A♭   F⁷   B♭   A♭   B♭⁷   E♭   B♭⁷   E♭
D   G   E⁷   A   G   A⁷   D   A⁷   D

30

SAILORS' HORNPIPE

Sea Shanty

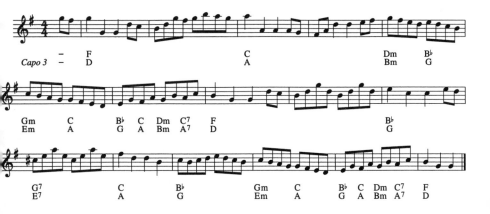

Capo 3

–	F		C		Dm	B♭
–	D		A		Bm	G

Gm	C	B♭	C	Dm	C⁷	F	B♭
Em	A	G	A	Bm	A⁷	D	G

G⁷	C	B♭	Gm	C	B♭	C	Dm	C⁷	F
E⁷	A	G	Em	A	G	A	Bm	A⁷	D

COUNTRY GARDENS

Traditional English Melody

C	F	G	C	Dm	G⁷	C

F	G	C	Dm	G⁷	C

Am	Em	Am	Em	Am	D	G

C	F	G	C	Dm	G⁷	C

31

BLACK EYES
Traditional Russian Melody

LILLIBURLERO
Traditional English Melody

THE TROUT QUINTET
Franz Schubert

I DO LIKE TO BE BESIDE THE SEASIDE

John Glover-Kind

PRELUDE

Frédéric Chopin

MY GRANDFATHER'S CLOCK
Henry Clay Work

EARLY ONE MORNING
Traditional English Melody

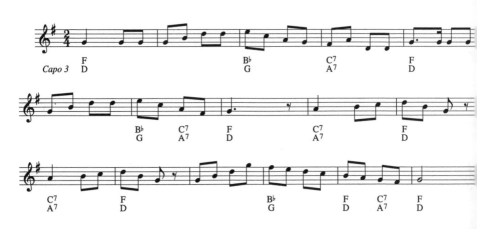

I'LL TAKE YOU HOME AGAIN, KATHLEEN

Thomas Westendorf

JOHN PEEL

Traditional English Melody

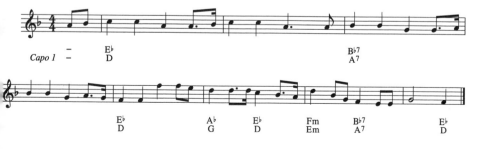

THEME from VIOLIN CONCERTO

Ludwig van Beethoven

VALSE LENTE from 'COPPÉLIA'

Léo Delibes

GALOP

Jacques Offenbach

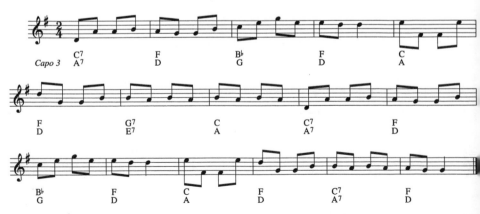

DOWN BY THE RIVERSIDE

Spiritual

NEW WORLD SYMPHONY (2nd Movement)

Antonín Dvořák

SHEEP MAY SAFELY GRAZE

Johann Sebastian Bach

AVE VERUM CORPUS

Wolfgang Amadeus Mozart

RADETZKY MARCH

Johann Strauss

Capo 1

	Eb
	D

Bb7	Eb	Bb	F7
A7	D	A	E7

Bb	Bb7	Eb
A	A7	D

F	C	Eb	Ab	Bb7	Eb
E	B	D	G	A7	D

MY BONNIE LIES OVER THE OCEAN

Traditional Melody

Capo 3

	C	F	C
	A	D	A

G	G7	C	F	C	F	G7
E	E7	A	D	A	D	E7

C	F	G	C
A	D	E	A

F	D7	G	G7	C
D	B7	E	E7	A

WALTZ

Johannes Brahms

WALTZ from 'DIE FLEDERMAUS'

Johann Strauss

THE ASH GROVE

Traditional Welsh Melody

PROMENADE from
'PICTURES AT AN EXHIBITION'

Modest Musorgsky

41

ALL THROUGH THE NIGHT

Traditional Welsh Melody

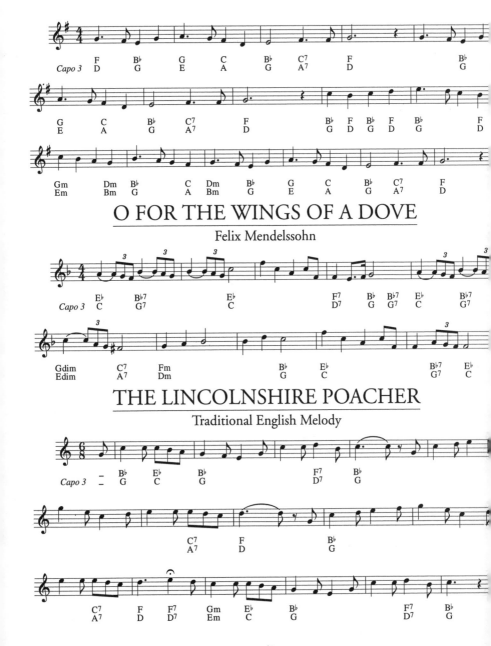

O FOR THE WINGS OF A DOVE

Felix Mendelssohn

THE LINCOLNSHIRE POACHER

Traditional English Melody

O MY BELOVED FATHER

Giacomo Puccini

Capo 3

| F | | | Fdim | F | | C | Gm7 |
| D | | | Ddim | D | | A | Em7 |

| Dm | G7 | | C | C7 | F |
| Bm | E7 | | A | A7 | D |

| Fdim | F | | Gm7 | C7 | Am | Dm | B♭ | Gm7 |
| Ddim | D | | Em7 | A7 | F#m | Bm | G | Em7 |

| Dm | B♭ | C7 | F | B♭maj7 | Gm7 | C7 | F |
| Bm | C | A7 | D | Gmaj7 | Em7 | A7 | D |

PAVANE

Gabriel Fauré

| Gm | E♭ | F | Dm | E♭ | Cm | D |

| Gm | | Cm | Fm | B♭7 | E♭ | D |

| Gm | E♭ | F | Dm | E♭ | Cm | D |

| Gm | B♭7 | E♭ | Fm | E♭7 | D7 | Gm |

43

POLLY-WOLLY-DOODLE

Traditional American Melody

CHARLIE IS MY DARLING

Traditional Scottish Melody

WHEN THE SAINTS GO MARCHING IN

Spiritual

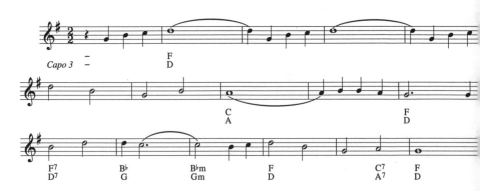

LA DONNA È MOBILE

Giuseppe Verdi

THE FLORAL DANCE

Traditional English Melody

BLUE DANUBE WALTZ

Johann Strauss

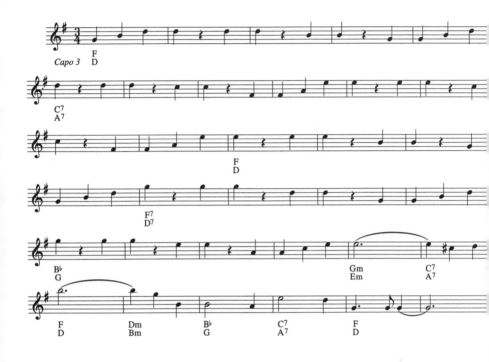

FOR HE'S A JOLLY GOOD FELLOW

Traditional English Melody

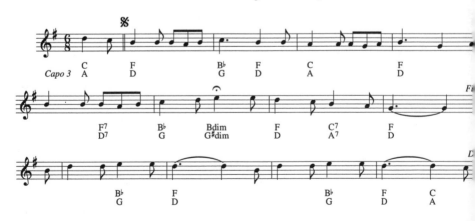

IT'S A LONG WAY TO TIPPERARY

Jack Judge and Harry Williams

LOCH LOMOND

Traditional Scottish Melody

ABIDE WITH ME

William Henry Monk

SWING LOW

Spiritual

GOODNIGHT LADIES

Traditional English Melody